My Classic Stories

The Ugly Duckling

This book belongs to

Age -------------

Enjoy this book,
love from The Ugly Duckling

This edition first published in 2013 by Ginger Fox Ltd
Copyright © 2013 Ginger Fox Ltd

Published in the UK by:
Ginger Fox Ltd
Stirling House, College Road
Cheltenham GL53 7HY
United Kingdom

www.gingerfox.co.uk

Retold by Nina Filipek
Illustrated by Katherine Kirkland

ISBN: 978-1-909290-06-8

10 9 8 7 6 5 4 3 2 1

Printed and bound in China.

GINGER
FOX

The Ugly Duckling

Once upon a time a mother duck
sat on her eggs.

Slowly, one by one, the eggs
cracked and out popped four
fluffy yellow ducklings.

Finally, only one egg was left.

The duckling that came out of
this egg was different –
it was grey and scruffy-looking.

The other farmyard animals made fun of the grey duckling and called him the 'ugly duckling'.

This made him very sad.

"Why am I different to my brothers and sisters?" he wondered.

The ugly duckling decided to run away to find some new friends because everyone on the farm was horrible to him.

9

Soon he came to a pond
where a family of geese lived.
They said he could stay with them.

But he was frightened when he heard
the sound of hunters firing shotguns.

He thought it
would be too
dangerous to
live there, so
he travelled on.

An old lady found the
ugly duckling and took
him back to her cottage.

Her dog
growled at him,
        her cat hissed at him
and her hen pecked at him.

They said,
 "Go away,
   ugly duckling.
    We don't want
      you here!"

"The old lady plans to eat you anyway!"

The ugly duckling felt lonelier than ever.

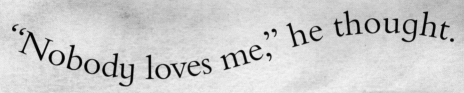

"Nobody loves me," he thought.

One day, the
ugly duckling was
standing by a lake
when he saw some
white swans fly past.
He thought they
looked beautiful.

'How I wish

I was a swan

instead of an

ugly duckling!"

he said to himself.

15

Winter came early that year.
It was bitterly cold and the lake froze over.
The ugly duckling tried to shelter in the reeds.

Then one morning, after a particularly cold
night, he woke up to find his feet were stuck
in the ice. He could not move.

He was cold and
very hungry.

A man was out walking when he saw the ugly duckling.

He freed him from the ice and took him home.

The kind man wrapped the
ugly duckling in a blanket
and warmed him in front
of the fire. Then he fed him
some tasty worms.

20

The ugly duckling was happy staying with the man. Winter turned to spring, and the snow started to melt. Then one day, the man's children chased the ugly duckling under a cupboard.

They only wanted to play with him, but he was scared and he ran away once more.

Many weeks passed and the days got warmer. The ugly duckling grew bigger, and saw the white swans again, swimming on the lake.

This time they came over to him and asked if he wanted to join them.

The ugly duckling
was surprised.

'Why do
they want to
play with me?
I'm just an ugly duckling!"

The ugly duckling bent his
head shyly. As he did so, he saw
his reflection in the water.

It shone
    back at him
        like a mirror.

            He was not an ugly
            duckling any more –

he was
a beautiful
white swan!

Can you remember?

Now that you have read the story,
try to answer these questions about it.

1. "Why did I run away from the farm?"

2. What did the old lady's hen do to the ugly duckling? Did it:

Peck him?

OR

High-five him?

3. Who rescued the ugly duckling from the ice? Was it:

A kind man?　　OR　　A family of geese?

4. Why was the ugly duckling afraid of the man's children?

5. What did the ugly duckling see when he bent his head and looked in the water?

Did you spot?

There is only one ugly duckling in this story,
but can you find these animals as well?
See if you can count them all.

1. Did you see ALL twenty-three
yellow chicks and ducklings?

 ?   2. Can you find the four frogs?

3. The old lady had one dog, but can you spot the other
three dogs in the story?

?

4. Looking back, can you find five mice?

5. Did you see the two dragonflies?
Where were they?

6. What were the pictures in the man's house of?

?

A sheep and   OR   A pig and
a horse?   a cow?

True or false?

Can you answer these true or false questions correctly?

1. The ugly duckling looks different to his brothers and sisters.
True or false?

2. The farmyard animals were kind to the ugly duckling.
True or false?

3. When winter came, the ugly duckling got stuck in the ice.
True or false?

4. A kind man fed the ugly duckling some biscuits.
True or false?

5. The ugly grey duckling grew to be a beautiful white swan.
True or false

Such a puzzle ...

Look carefully at the pictures below
and then try to answer the questions.

1. What are the dog and the cat doing in this picture?

?

2. What is
   different
   about this
   picture?

Take a look
back and
compare it
to the page
in the story
if you are
not sure.

Complete your collection ...

The Ugly Duckling

The Three Billy Goats Gruff

Hansel and Gretel

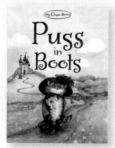
Puss in Boots

Little Red Riding Hood

Jack and the Beanstalk

Cinderella

The Gingerbread Man

The Emperor's New Clothes

Goldilocks and the Three Bears

Rapunzel

The Three Little Pigs

"Which one will you read next?"